CHARIOTS FOR Snoopy HIRE

by Charles M. Schulz

RAVETTE BOOKS

This edition first published by
Ravette Books Limited 1988

Printed in Great Britain
for Ravette Books Limited,
3 Glenside Estate, Star Road, Partridge Green,
Horsham, West Sussex RH13 8RA
by The Guernsey Press Company Limited,
Guernsey, Channel Islands,
and bound by
WBC Bookbinders Limited,
Maesteg, Mid Glamorgan.

ISBN 1 85304 059 2

SNOOPY

History is full of famous beagles. There was Alexander Beagle the Great, Leonardo da Beagle the artist and Ludwig Van Beaglehoven the composer. You can learn about these and other great beagles in history books. To learn about the adventures of today's most famous beagle, Snoopy, just read on...

HERE'S THE WORLD FAMOUS SERGEANT-MAJOR OF THE FOREIGN LEGION LEADING HIS TROOPS ON A MISSION

AS THEY LEAVE CIVILIZATION, THEY APPROACH THE DESERT WITH ITS MILES AND MILES OF BURNING SAND...

© 1983 United Feature Syndicate, Inc.   8-5

WELL, MAYBE THREE OR FOUR FEET

WOW! THAT'S A TOUGH QUESTION...HMM..LET ME THINK...HMM...

1-4-85

I HAVE TO SAY, GEORGE WASHINGTON

I'M RIGHT?! WHEW! WHAT A RELIEF...

© 1984 United Feature Syndicate, Inc.

YOU DROVE ME TO THE WARNING TRACK ON THAT ONE, MA'AM

HERE, ANOTHER LETTER FROM YOUR BROTHER SPIKE..

1-5-85

"DEAR SNOOPY, LIFE HERE ON THE DESERT IS GOOD... THE REAL ESTATE BUSINESS, HOWEVER, HAS BEEN SLOW..."

"I AM HOPING THAT MY NEW LOCATION WILL HELP"

© 1984 United Feature Syndicate, Inc.

HIPPITY-HOP

BUNNIES HIPPITY-HOP... DOGS DON'T HIPPITY-HOP..

1-21

TAKE ADVANTAGE OF THIS OFFER NOW!

SEND US YOUR NAME TODAY!

BUT YOU MUST BE 18 OR OLDER

WAIT FOR ME!

2-4 © 1985 United Feature Syndicate, Inc.

2-5

© 1985 United Feature Syndicate, Inc.

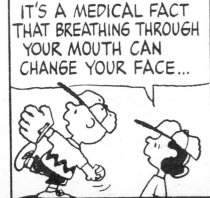

I LOVE GOING OVER TO WOODSTOCK'S NEST TO WATCH TV...

5-10

© 1985 United Feature Syndicate, Inc.

HE'S THE ONLY ONE WHO HAS A SATELLITE DISH..

THIS IS A GREAT GOLF HOLE..ONE OF THE BEST IN THE WORLD...

5-11

THE FAIRWAY IS LINED WITH BEAUTIFUL OAK AND PINE TREES...

THE WHITE SAND IN THE BUNKERS SPARKLES IN CONTRAST TO THE DEEP SHADES OF THE GREEN...

BEFORE I PLAY A HOLE, I ALWAYS FLATTER IT!

© 1985 United Feature Syndicate, Inc.

5-22

I WAS PRAYING FOR GREATER PATIENCE AND UNDERSTANDING, BUT I QUIT...

I WAS AFRAID I MIGHT GET IT

I CAN SEE MYSELF IN MY WATER DISH

IF I DRANK ALL THE WATER, I COULDN'T SEE MYSELF...

I'M VERY THIRSTY, TOO

BUT I'D RATHER LOOK AT MYSELF!

5-23

YES, MA'AM...SHE'S ASLEEP AGAIN...

NO, MA'AM..SHE CAN'T SLIDE UNDER THE DESK..

THERE'S A SAFETY CATCH...

5-24

SCHULZ

I WANT TO BE LIKED FOR MYSELF..

I DON'T WANT TO BE LIKED BECAUSE I KNOW THE RIGHT PEOPLE

5-25

I WANT TO BE LIKED FOR ME!

WHO?

SCHULZ

MY GRAMPA GOT INTO TROUBLE AT THE GOLF COURSE YESTERDAY...

5-27

WHEN HE DROVE UP TO THE CLUBHOUSE, HE SAW A SIGN THAT SAID, "HANDICAP PARKING"

HE SAID, "MY HANDICAP IS FIFTEEN"... SO HE PARKED THERE!

© 1985 United Feature Syndicate.inc

IN THE GAME OF LIFE, GRAMPA HAS A STRING OF DOUBLE BOGEYS...

THESE ARE "DELETE" SIGNS

THEY LOOK NICE.. IF I EVER NEED SOMETHING DELETED, I'LL CALL YOU...

5-28

I'D LOVE TO DO IT!

© 1985 United Feature Syndicate, Inc

Report: What I learned in school this year.

If I'm lucky, I'll be out in ten years.

5-31 © 1985 United Feature Syndicate, Inc.

TEMPTING BUT RISKY..

IF THAT BACK DOOR OPENS, I GET SUPPER.. IF IT DOESN'T, I STARVE TO DEATH!

I CAN'T BELIEVE MY WHOLE LIFE DEPENDS ON A BACK DOOR...

6-1 © 1985 United Feature Syndicate, Inc.

STUPID DOOR

IT'S STILL RAINING SO WE'RE SUPPOSED TO GO OVER TO THE REC HALL FOR A SING-A-LONG...

WHAT'S A SING-A-LONG?

A COUNSELOR LEADS THE SINGING..SHE'LL SAY, "OH, COME ON, YOU CAN SING LOUDER THAN THAT!" THEN SHE'LL WANT US TO CLAP OUR HANDS...

© 1985 United Feature Syndicate, Inc.

THEN SHE'LL SAY, "C'MON, BOYS, LET'S SEE IF YOU CAN SING LOUDER THAN THE GIRLS! C'MON, GIRLS.. SHOW THE BOYS HOW LOUD YOU CAN SING!"

6-19

I THINK I'LL JUST STAND OUT HERE IN THE RAIN..

YES, SIR.. I WANT MY MONEY BACK..THIS IS THE WORST SUMMER CAMP I'VE EVER BEEN TO!

IF YOU DON'T GIVE ME MY MONEY BACK, I'M GOING TO SUE!

ALL IT DOES IS RAIN! IT'S TOO WET TO ENJOY ANYTHING! EVEN MY ATTORNEY THINKS IT'S TOO WET...

6-20 © 1985 United Feature Syndicate, Inc.

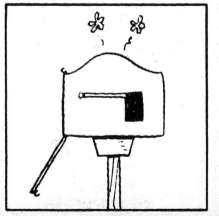

Other Snoopy titles published by Ravette Books

Black and white landscapes
It's a Dog's Life	£2.50
Roundup	£2.50
Freewheelin'	£2.50
Joe Cool	£2.50
Dogs Don't Eat Dessert	£2.50
You're on the Wrong Foot Again, Charlie Brown	£2.50

Snoopy Stars
No. 1	Snoopy Stars as The Flying Ace	£1.95
No. 2	Snoopy Stars as The Matchmaker	£1.95
No. 3	Snoopy Stars as The Terror of the Ice	£1.95
No. 4	Snoopy Stars as The Legal Beagle	£1.95
No. 5	Snoopy Stars as The Fearless Leader	£1.95
No. 6	Snoopy Stars as Man's Best Friend	£1.95
No. 7	Snoopy Stars as The Sportsman	£1.95
No. 8	Snoopy Stars as The Scourge of the Fairways	£1.95
No. 9	Snoopy Stars as The Branch Manager	£1.95
No. 10	Snoopy Stars as The World Famous Literary Ace	£1.95
No. 11	Snoopy Stars as The Great Pretender	£1.95
No. 12	Snoopy Stars as The Dog-Dish Gourmet	£1.95

Colour landscapes
First Serve	£2.95
Be Prepared	£2.95
Stay Cool	£2.95
Shall We Dance?	£2.95
Let's Go	£2.95
Come Fly With Me	£2.95

Weekenders
No. 1	Weekender	£4.95

All these books are available at your local bookshop or newsagent, or can be ordered direct from the publisher. Just tick the titles you require and fill in the form below. Prices and availability subject to change without notice.

Ravette Books Limited, 3 Glenside Estate, Star Road, Partridge Green, Horsham, West Sussex RH13 8RA

Please send a cheque or postal order, and allow the following for postage and packing. UK: 45p for one book plus 30p for each additional book.

Name ....

Address ....

....